Haiku poetry

a children's collection

Written and Illustrated
by Children of

THE WILHELM SCHOLÊ

An American School
for Children of all Nations

BANTAM BOOKS
TORONTO · NEW YORK · LONDON

RLI: $\dfrac{\text{VLM 4 (VLR 4-6)}}{\text{IL 4-8}}$

HAIKU POETRY: A CHILDREN'S COLLECTION
*A Bantam Book / published by arrangement with
The Wilhelm School*

PRINTING HISTORY
*The Wilhelm School edition published December 1971
2nd printing . . . February 1975   3rd printing . . . November 1975
Bantam edition / June 1978*

ISBN 0-553-11809-9

Published simultaneously in the United States and Canada

"The Reward of Learning is Happiness"

Wilhelm Scholê Motto

THE WILHELM SCHOLÊ

The Wilhelm Scholê in Houston, Texas, is one of the most extraordinary I have ever known. Its general philosophy is that traditional education has undereducated and underestimated children and that the aesthetic experience is a part of the foundation of a creative adult existence.

From its inception the thrust of the Wilhelm Scholê has been to educate children through the arts, which illuminate all societies, and to tie the arts into the sciences, mathematics, religion, and the story of civilization from its beginning; starting in Africa and Asia as our oldest cultures, moving from there into the Greek and Roman eras which made way for our modern world.

The Wilhelm Scholê has two fine accomplishments. Their two- and three-year-olds are learning more than I did at the age of six, when I was permitted to enter primary school. The second achievement is that the children are not taking courses that run parallel to each other but never touch. All of their subjects are integrated, so that they are learning about life as a whole and not as a series of fragmented disciplines. What better way to learn about botany than to become skilled in Japanese floral arrangements? What better way to study ancient history than to fly to New Orleans and spend a full day at the King Tut exhibition, and then to write an essay on the meaning and emotional impact of the experience?

It has long been my contention that in order to teach students how to read, it is first necessary to teach them how to write. At the Wilhelm Scholê all the children write every day, the older ones teaching the two- and three-year-olds not only how to write, but how to express themselves. With every-day writing being the norm, the students naturally read every day. On music, which they play, on architecture, which they observe, on mathematics, technology, medicine, and geography, which even the three- and four-year-olds are able to grasp and fit into their picture of themselves as members of the human race, in all of its nationalities, religions, cultures, so that they learn to see life entire, and to understand that all history is contemporary.

One further word has to be added: I have never seen young children so happy, so stimulated and excited, so content to be in school. The Wilhelm Scholê challenges, feeds, trains their minds to their outermost capacity. No discipline is needed here; joy is the greatest of all disciplines. The joy of learning, understanding, of identifying with all peoples and places in history is the bedrock on which the Wilhelm Scholê is founded.

It is my earnest hope that its methods will spread through our land. Then no longer will we be harassed by the question, "Why can't Johnny read?" Johnny will read because Johnny will write, every day, on some fascinating aspect of his fellow man's accomplishments, each part organically linked to the whole. That is what the Wilhelm Scholê is about.

Irving Stone
February 7, 1978

ACKNOWLEDGMENTS

The Wilhelm Scholê wishes to thank
Mrs. Jean Sano, wife of the First Japanese
Consul to Houston, Texas, and other members
of the Japanese community in Houston
who selected the winners of the Haiku Awards.

Calligraphy by Anna Marie Jurek.

PREFACE

Education begins with poetry.
—Confucius

At Wilhelm Scholê we, too, begin education through poetry. Poetry in China, as in Greece, was the language of the gods. It was poetry that inculcated laws and maxims. When memory took the place of writing, it was through the harmony of poetic lines that traditions were handed down. It was and remains the first language of wisdom and inspiration.

This ancient tradition of using poetry as an educational force is shared by the Wilhelm Scholê, where we are planting a love of wisdom in the minds and hearts of our students by having them commit to memory aphorisms of the world's great thinkers, leaders, teachers, and saints. It is our cherished hope that these life-building, character-making ideas will nourish them throughout their lives.

However, it is not only memory but mastery we are striving for. We believe that at a very early age the child should learn that every step of learning as well as everything in life can be expressed in the language of beauty. Further, we have found that poetry leads to brotherhood and to an understanding of the oneness of humanity. For by studying the great poets of other cultures and other ages, our students now identify intellectually, spiritually, and aesthetically with those whose way of life differs entirely from their own. An example of this exposure and enlightenment is our book of Haiku poetry.

"Where children are," Novalis remarked, "there is the Golden Age." I live in the truth of these words at The Wilhelm Scholê, where the children's atmosphere of sincerity, gaiety, simplicity, and hope is contagious. Their attitude that each experience is an adventure and their capacity to share delicate intuitions are manifest in this book of Haiku poems.

May we all enter into that Golden Age with these children and share their enthusiasm for the magic and wonder of being alive.

Marilyn E. Wilhelm
Founder-Director
The Wilhelm Scholê

January 1978
Houston, Texas

*He who aspires to be a great poet
must first become a little child.*

Macaulay

THE WIND BLOWS MY HAIR
MAKES MY FACE SMOOTH AND CLEAN
AND JUST FEELING GOOD.

KEVIN NUNEZ 7YRS

FRIENDLY CLOUDS ABOVE
GRASS BLOWING IN THE COOL RAIN
SWISH, SWISH, SWISH, SWISH, SWISH

TOMMY BOYD 7YRS

RAINY, RAINY DAY
SMALL ANT SLIDING UP AND DOWN
SLIPPERY, SLIPPERY POLE!

ALLISON HENNESSY 6YRS

GRASSHOPPER JUMPING
PLAYING IN THE TALL WET GRASS
OH! RAIN SENDS HIM HOME

LARA LOPEZ 5YRS

PUDDLE TO PUDDLE
CRICKETS PLAYFULLY JUMPING
HAPPY RAINY DAY

TOMMY BOYD 7YRS

OH SWEET LITTLE BIRD
FLYING IN THE SKY SO HIGH
WATCH OUT FOR THE RAIN

CHRIS TOMEK 8 YRS

TENTH AWARD
1975

SAD, SAD INSECT
SO LONELY...NOTHING TO DO
RAINDROPS AND TEARDROPS

              TODD THURBER 6YRS

SO HIGH IN THE SKY
AND SO VERY, VERY DARK
HOW CAN I REACH YOU?

           JALEH RAVASSIPOUR 5YRS

TALL FLOWERS SWAYING
KISSED BY GENTLE DROPS OF RAIN
LOVE COMES FROM HEAVEN

        CHRIS DOOYEMA 6YRS

HAPPY BLOSSOMING
FLOWERS LIFT THEIR HEADS IN THANKS
FOR NATURE'S GIFT OF RAIN

         JOHN DORA 5YRS
         MICHELLE JERNIGAN
             7YRS

ANGRY WINDS BLOWING
MOTHER AND CHILD SAFELY HELD
STRONG YET TENDER TREE

                    TODO FRAZIER 5yrs

    LIGHTNING FLASHES
    BABY UNDER MOTHER'S WING
    SAFE AND UNAFRAID

                    CHIQUITA WILLIS 5yrs

SMALL RED ANTS CRAWLING
ALL OVER THEIR MUDDY HOUSE
DO NOT GET STUCK ANTS!

                    SUSAN MAHAN 6yrs

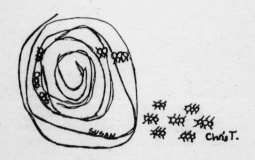

SEVENTH AWARD
1975

BEAUTIFUL PICTURE.....
WET GREEN GRASS PAINTED BY RAIN
SHINING SUN RETURNS

RYOKO YUTA 4YRS.

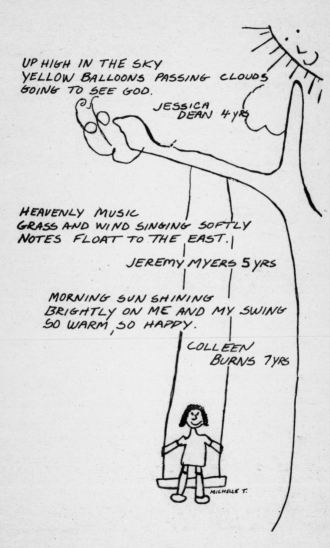

UP HIGH IN THE SKY
YELLOW BALLOONS PASSING CLOUDS
GOING TO SEE GOD.

JESSICA
DEAN 4 YRS

HEAVENLY MUSIC
GRASS AND WIND SINGING SOFTLY
NOTES FLOAT TO THE EAST.

JEREMY MYERS 5 YRS

MORNING SUN SHINING
BRIGHTLY ON ME AND MY SWING
SO WARM, SO HAPPY.

COLLEEN
BURNS 7 YRS

MICHELLE T.

7

WHITE COTTON CANDY
SCATTERED BY WARM BLOWING WIND
EATEN BY THE SKY.

RANDY KEELING 6YRS

BLUE SKY, SILENT TREE
FLUTTERING BIRDS AWAKEN
CHIRP, CHIRP FILLS THE AIR.

GARTH LUTHER 5yrs

LITTLE BIRD IN TREE
RESTING IN ITS NEST, DREAMING...
OF FRIENDS FAR AWAY.

JASON KUTTNER COHN 5yrs

CLOUDLESS SUNNY DAY
BIRDS SINGING TO BRIGHT BLUE SKY
MELODIES OF PEACE.

MICHELLE JERNIGAN 7yrs

PRETTY LITTLE BIRD
ARE YOU LOOKING FOR A WORM?
COME, I WILL FEED YOU.

GAIL BLAHUTA 4yrs
PAIGE WALDROP 7yrs

TRAVIS

MOTHER FLYING HOME
BRINGING LOTS OF WORMS TO EAT
FAT LITTLE BABIES

> CLARA PYBUS 5yrs

SMALL BIRD TRIES TO FLY
FLUTTER, FLUTTER, FLUTTER, PLOP
NEST SEEMS FAR AWAY

> TRAE MULLIGAN 5yrs

BROTHER AND SISTER....
BLUE WINGS FLAPPING IN THE SKY
QUICKLY GOING HOME.

> LENORA SUKI 5yrs

BABIES TRYING WINGS
MOTHER TEACHES, TREE WATCHES
WE ARE GROWING UP!

> SYLVIA CANO
> 4yrs

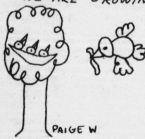

PAIGE W

SAD BABY BLUE BIRD
LOOKING, WATCHING, WONDERING
WHERE IS MY MOTHER?

      LEVON VARTANIAN 7yrs

BIRD FLYING, SINGING
LOOKING, SEARCHING FOR FOOD
BABIES WAIT AT HOME

      VIKRAM VIJAYVERGIYA 6yrs

BRIGHT SUNNY MORNING
HUNGRY BABIES, OPEN MOUTHS...
FATHER EAGLE COMES.

      GREG PARISH 7yrs

BLUE BIRD ON THE BRANCH
SINGING SWEET SONGS TO HIS MATE
LOVE IS IN THE AIR.

PRISCILLA MARIE RAINEY
4 YRS

**SIXTH AWARD
1975**

GREEN TREES, BLADES OF GRASS
SMALL BIRDS AND PRETTY FLOWERS
NATURE BEAUTIFUL!

VIKRAM VIJAYVERGIYA 6 yrs

WILD BLACK BIRDS AND I
MAKING SHADOWS IN SUNSHINE
WHAT A HAPPY DAY!

KAREN KEELING 7 yrs

TINY RED BIRD
PLYING QUICKLY UP AND DOWN
CHASING A SPARROW.

CHYRISSA STALEY 4 yrs.

BIRDS PLAYING HIDE AND SEEK
LEAVES AND SHADOWS... SECRET PLACES
HAPPY AFTERNOON!

JASON KUTTNER COHN 5 yrs

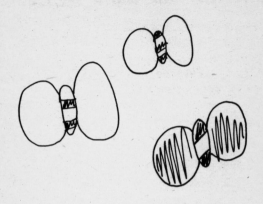

BUZZ, BUZZ, BUZZ, BUZZ, BUZZ
ALL I HEAR IS BUZZ, BUZZ, BUZZ
BUZZ, BUZZ, BUZZ, BUZZ, BUZZ

MICHELLE TOMEK
7YRS.

SLOW SMALL ANIMAL
SECRET WEAPON MAKES HIM STRONG
WATCH OUT FOR WHITE STRIPES

TRACY DUNHAM 6YRS

DANCING HONEY BEE
FINDS TREASURES FOR ALL TO SHARE
DELICIOUS NECTAR.

JENNIFER YBARRA 8YRS

BUSY HONEY BEE
BOWING, WORKING FOR THE QUEEN
EVERY SINGLE DAY.

CHRIS TOMEK 8YRS

IN OUR SUNNY YARD
MY DOG FRODO SOMERSAULTS
HAPPY DOG PLAYING!

JESSICA KOONCE
3 YRS
CHRIS DOOYEMA
6 YRS

15

ONE BRIGHT SUNNY DAY
HOT WIND BLOWING GRASS
SILENTLY WAVING.

BRANDON BOEHM
7 YRS.

GARTH

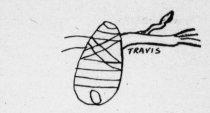

LITTLE HONEYBEE
BUZZING ON A WINDOW
MAKING FUNNY SOUNDS

TRAE MULLIGAN 5yrs

HOUSEFLY AND HONEYBEE
SHARING SOMETHING GOOD TO EAT
SWEET CHOCOLATE CAKE

HARRY BARTHOLOMEW 5yrs

HONEY BEE WORKING
BRINGING POLLEN TO THE HIVE
NUTRITIOUS DINNER!

ANNA MARIA SAHAKIAN 4yrs
TRAVIS BROUSSARD. 6yrs

SUCH A PRETTY DAY
BEES BUZZING BY THE GRASS
PLAYING WITH THEIR FRIENDS

STACY SCHWING 5yrs.

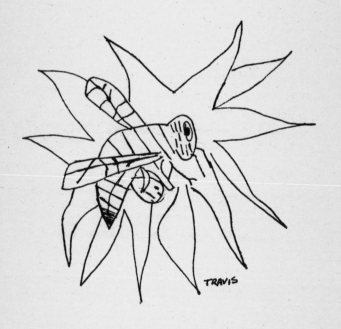

TRAVIS

EIGHTH AWARD
1975

HONEY BEE WORKING
KNEE DEEP IN SUNFLOWER DUST
NECTAR FOR THE QUEEN.

WESLEY SETTLE 4yrs

FIFTH AWARD
1971

BLACK AND YELLOW STRIPES
FLYING, LOOKING FOR NECTAR
BUZZING, BUZZING BEES.

TODD THURBER 6yrs

TWELFTH AWARD
1975

BUSY LITTLE BEE
BRINGING THE YELLOW POLLEN
HELPING SEEDS TO GROW.

ROBBI ZUBER 5yrs

VIOLET, GREEN, YELLOW
WINGS FLUTTERING IN THE AIR
LIFE IS BEAUTIFUL

MITRA MECHANIC 5yrs

TODD F.

YELLOW ON YELLOW
BUTTERCUP HIDES BUTTERFLY
NATURE SPEAKS OF LOVE

MICHELLE WERCH 6YRS

ORANGE BUTTERFLY
FLYING, FLOATING AND PLAYING
ALWAYS HAVING FUN

GARTH LUTHER 5YRS

WARM AND SUNNY DAY
RED BUTTERFLIES IN MY HAIR
PLAYING ON MY HEAD

YVONNE LO 6YRS

BUTTERFLIES PLAYING
RING AROUND THE YELLOW ROSE
PETALS ALL FALL DOWN

TANYA QUEBE 6YRS

JENNIFER

NINTH AWARD
1975

WIND SOFTLY BLOWING
DANCING WITH RED BUTTERFLY
HAPPY JOURNEY HOME

            MICHELLE WERCH 6YRS

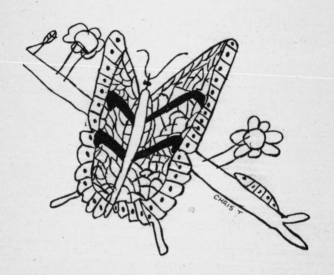

COLLEEN

DRAGONFLY BUZZES
CIRCLING ON TOP OF THE WIND
WITHOUT MAKING SOUNDS

STEPHEN RICHARDSON 8yrs

DRAGONFLIES GO UP
BUTTERFLIES GO DOWN SLOWLY
MOVEMENTS SO VERY PRETTY

EVALYN LAING 7yrs

A DRAGONFLY FLEW
OVER MY HEAD AND LANDED
THEN IT DISAPPEARED

TODD THURBER 6yrs

LITTLE DRAGONFLY
FLYING WITH FAVORITE FRIEND
WHERE ARE YOU GOING?

TAKU YOSHIDA 4yrs

TODD I

ANCIENT TREE IN PARK
HOLDING SMALL CATERPILLAR
CRAWLING TO HIS MEAL.

COLLEEN BURNS 7yrs

FIRST AWARD
1971

VIOLINIST PLAYING
LOVE SONGS TO HIS LONELY MATE
CRICKET CRIES NO MORE.

MICHELLE JERNIGAN 7yrs

ACROBAT LEAPS HIGH
BLADE OF GRASS MAKES FINE TRAPEZE
GOOD INSECT CIRCUS!

LENORA SUKI 5yrs

GRASS HIDING HUNTER
CURIOUS FLY PASSES BY
CHAMP, CHAMP...GONE IS FLY

JENNIFER YBARRA 8yrs

GREEN BODY, BLACK TAIL
GIGANTIC GRASSHOPPER JUMPS
AND SWALLOWS A BUG.

BRANDON BOEHM 8yrs

KIYOSHI

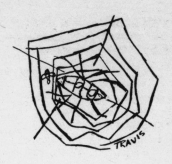

EIGHT BLACK HAIRY LEGS
CRAWLING THROUGH LACY WHITE HOUSE
SEARCHING FOR A FLY.
                TRAVIS BROUSSARD 6YRS

BLACK AND GREY SPIDER
QUICKLY SPINNING ROUND AND ROUND
TINY STICKY WEB
                VIKAS BHUSHAN 4YRS

BLACK AND BROWN SPIDER
PLAYING IN MY COFFEE CAN
DO A TRICK FOR ME.
                GARY COOK 6YRS

BIG FEET WALKING FAST
TINY CLOUDS OF FRIGHTENED GNATS
QUICKLY DISAPPEARS

ANTHONY STIRLING 6YRS

TWO FRIENDLY FLOWERS
WATCHING ANTS MAKE A HOME
SUN SHINING BRIGHTLY

ERMELINDA CUELLAR 5YRS

SOLDIERS SEEK AND FIND
MARCHING IN THE FLOWERBED
TREASURE FOR THE QUEEN

LOUIS GIRARD 5YRS

ANTS SLEEPING IN BED
NIGHTMARES OF BIG STOMPING FEET
SO VERY FRIGHTENED

GARY COOK 6YRS

COLLEEN

BIG BROWN MOTHER FROG
STUCK IN A VERY SMALL HOLE
LET ME HELP YOU OUT!

VIKRAM VIJAYVERGIYA
6yrs

FROG HOPPING AND JUMPING
SMALL CHILD OUT TO FIND A FRIEND
OH! HE JUMPS AWAY

            ROBIN BENNETT 5yrs

PLAYING IN THE FLOWERS
FOUND A FROG AND MADE A FRIEND
HER NAME IS BETSY

          MICHELE DEGUERIN 6yrs

HEALTHY LITTLE FROG
JUMPING AND JOGGING AROUND
IN MY HAPPY HOUSE.

           BRANDON BOEHM 8yrs

CROAK, CROAK, JUMP, JUMP, CROAK
HUNTER LOOKING FOR A FLY...
DELICIOUS BREAKFAST!

           JULIE WHARTON 6yrs

FIFTH AWARD
1975

TUMBLING AND WRESTLING
PUPPIES PLAYING IN THE YARD
SUMMERTIME IS FUN!

SEAN COBB 5YRS

JASON

BOY WALKING WITH DOG
SUN SMILING ON FAVORITE FRIENDS
HAPPY SUMMER DAY!

TROY NICHOLAS 6YRS

FUZZY BALL OF FUR
HAVING GOOD TIME IN THE PARK
ROLLING IN THE SAND.

JOHN SAHAKIAN 5YRS

DOG CHASING BRAVE CAT...
UP THE TREE LIKE A TIGER
OUR HERO IS SAFE.

REYNALDO CARDONA
6YRS

CAT CHASING BLUE BIRD
RUNNING UP THE TREE SO FAST
HUNGRY CAT NEEDS WINGS

AUDREY CHANG 3YRS

MICHELLE JERNIGAN
7YRS

TRAVIS

GREG

YELLOW MOTHER DUCK
SITTING ON HER NEST, DREAMING
FOR A BABY BOY
                    CAMILLE ORENGO 5yrs

CHICKEN SITS ON NEST
BABIES ARE HATCHING IN EGGS
A HAPPY BIRTHDAY!
                    CHAD PAYNE 5yrs

FUZZY BABY CHICK
MOTHER HELPING SCRATCH FOR FOOD
BABY SCRATCHES TOO.
                    LISA SILVERMAN 3yrs
                    ROBIN BELL 7yrs

FARMER SEES A SHELL
EATING IN THE LETTUCE PATCH
HUNGRY TURTLE HIDES
                    ANNA MARIA SAHAKIAN
                    LEVON VARTANIAN 4yrs
                              7yrs

YVONNE

MY PUPPIES AND I
PLAYING RUN AND CATCH THE BALL
HAPPY SUNNY DAY !

> BECKY BARROS   4 yrs.
> JASON KUTTNER COHN 5 yrs

HIGH ON THE BRANCHES
PICKING AND EATING PECANS
BUSY, BUSY SQUIRREL

> MARTI ROBERTS 5 yrs.

GREY SQUIRRELS PLAYING
FOLLOW THE LEADER ABOVE
A HUNGRY SPARROW.

> TODD THURBER 6 yrs

IN THE GARDEN PATCH
CARROTS, CABBAGE, AND LETTUCE
RABBIT IS IN HEAVEN

> SCOTT WALKER 4 yrs
> MICHELLE WERCH 6 yrs
> JULIE WHARTON 6 yrs

SNOW SILENTLY FALLS
WINTER HOMES WITH SLEEPING BEARS
CUDDLING AND DREAMING
                    LEVON VARTANIAN 7yrs

YAWNING AND STRETCHING
BEARS AWAKEN TO SPRINGTIME
BLOSSOMS FRESH AND SWEET
                    KIYOSHI YUTA 7yrs

BEARS IN THE TREE HOUSE
SLEEPING ON A WINTER NIGHT
OWLS CALL WHOOO WHOOO WHOOO
                    WILL PETERMAN 3yrs
                    PAIGE WALDROP 7yrs

Chris Tomek

CURIOUS.... SILENT
LONG THIN NECK PEEKS IN THE TREE
SEES BABIES SLEEP

        KIM WHITTLESEY 4YRS

ACROBAT SWINGING
ARM OVER ARM THROUGH THE TREES
JUNGLE LIFE IS FUN

        RUSSELL WEIGL 6YRS

TO THE MARKETPLACE
FLAT FEET ARE MARCHING
DESERT CARAVAN

        CURTIS CONRAD 6YRS

BEAUTIFUL ROSEBUD
PLEASE OPEN YOUR HEART AND BLOOM
WHY ARE YOU SO SHY.?

ANDREA BAHR 6yrs

PAIGE M.

PRETTY PINK ROSEBUD
BRINGING BEAUTY TO THE WORLD
HELPING US TO LIVE

> JENNIFER FISHER 5yrs

TWO BIG RED ROSES
GROWING HAPPILY IN THE PARK
WATCH PEOPLE PASS BY

> KATHRYN KEETCH 5yrs

PURPLE ROSE FLOWERS
OH, HOW YOU GROW SO CROOKED
IN AND OUT OF THE FENCE

> KAREN KEELING 7yrs

PURPLE, BLUE FLOWER
LOOKING HIGH OVER THE FENCE
WISHING FOR A FRIEND

> SUSAN WILSON 4yrs

MAGNOLIAS BLOOMING
LEMON SCENTS FLOAT IN THE AIR
GREEN AND WHITE BOUQUET

       LOUIS GIRARD 5yrs
       TROY NICHOLAS 6yrs

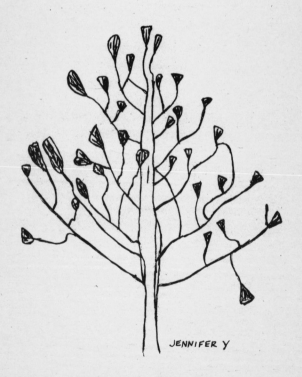

JENNIFER Y

SWAYING IN THE WIND
MANY FLOWERS ARE DANCING
THEY SEEM SO HAPPY

STEVEN SAENZ 5YRS

SUNFLOWER GROWING
STRETCHING, REACHING FOR THE SKY
TRYING TO FIND GOD

MONICA VARNER 5YRS

SUN'S FAVORITE FLOWERS
IN THE GARDEN SUNBATHING
GROWING TALL AND STRONG

MICHAEL MANAHAN 5YRS

I SEE BUTTERCUPS
IN THE SUN MAKING NEW FRIENDS
LOVE IS HAPPINESS!

DAWN STEVENS
5YRS

TRAVIS

ALL THE LEAVES ARE GONE
AND IT IS VERY LONELY...
A MINNOW SWIMS BY

MICHELE DEGUERIN 6yrs

WINTER WIND BLOWING
LONELY BIRD FLYING AWAY
TWEET, TWEET, TWEET, TWEET, TWEET

        PAIGE MARTIN 6YRS

WIND PLAYING LOVE SONGS
MUSIC FOR DANCING LEAVES
TREE WHISPERS GOODBY

        ROBIN BELL 7YRS

LEAVES MAKING SHADOWS
QUICKLY MOVING UP AND DOWN
WAVING TO THE SKY

        SHEILA BURNS 6YRS

PEEKING THROUGH THE LEAVES
PINK EYES AND LONG FLOPPY EARS
WHITE COATS TURN TO BROWN

        PAIGE MARTIN 5YRS

LEVON

COLD WINDS, BLOWING LEAVES
AND FLOCKS OF BIRDS FLYING SOUTH
MAYBE IT WILL SNOW

YVONNE LO 5yRS

WINTER WINDS BLOWING
MAKES MY FEET VERY COLD
IN COLD I GO HOME

VIKRAM VIJAYVERGIYA 6yRS

KIND TREE SHARES CLOTHING
WARMING THE SHIVERING EARTH
BROWN, YELLOW BLANKET

RACHEL WESTHEIMER
4yRS
PAIGE WALDROP 7yRS

REY

LOOKING FOR HER FRIEND
LADYBUG ON MY FINGER
TRAVELING ROUND AND ROUND

> ANNA LEON 3YRS
> JASON KUTTNER COHN
> 5YRS

WALKING HAND IN HAND
LADYBUGS TELLING SECRETS
FRIENDS ARE HAVING FUN!

> REYNALDO CARDONA
> 5YRS

WALLS SO VERY THIN
HUGGED MY MOUSEFRIEND GOODNIGHT
DO I HEAR A SCRATCHING?

> MICHELE DE GUERIN
> 6YRS

SOMEONE TOOK MY CHEESE
MY STOMACH BEGINS TO HURT
WALLS CLOSE IN ON ME.

> JOHN DURFEY 6YRS

43

FIRST AWARD
1975

TINY BOAT SAILING
WATER SMOOTH AS CRYSTAL
REFLECTS LONELINESS

PAIGE WALDROP 7yrs

KIYOSHI

GREEN AND BLACK DRAGON
ALWAYS HIDING IN THE CLOUDS
WISE AND ANCIENT KING

TRAVIS BROUSSARD
6YRS

MAJESTIC SYMBOL
SEEN YET HIDDEN IN THE CLOUDS
DRAGON OF WISDOM

DANNY McGINTY 6yrs

HIDDEN IN THE SEAWEED
AN UNDERWATER RAINBOW.....
BABY ANGEL FISH!

ALLISON FRAZIER 3yrs
JENNIFER YBARRA 8yrs

ORANGE BALL OF FIRE
SLOWLY SWALLOWED BY THE SEA
AWAY, FAR AWAY

RHONDA GLEASON 8yrs

FOURTH AWARD
1975

GENTLE OCEAN WAVES
MUSIC PLAYING WITHOUT END
NATURE'S SHELL OF PEACE

ROBIN BELL 7yrs

WARM SUMMER SUNDAY
SUN SHINING ON SPARKLING SAND
A PRETTY SEASHELL
                    LISA WILLIAMS 7YRS

RED STRIPES AND WHITE STRIPES
PEPPERMINT CANDY TO CRABS...
TIDE GOES OUT SLOWLY.
                MICHELLE JERNIGAN
                            7YRS

SWIMMING IN THE RIVER
FATHER FISH KEEPS BABIES SAFE
HAPPY FAMILY.
                    REYNALDO CARDONA
                            5YRS

FROM THE OCEAN BLUE
A PINK BALLOON IS RISING
OH! A JELLYFISH!
                    AMARIS LOPEZ 3YRS
                    GREG PARISH 7YRS

BUBBLE GUM WRAPPERS
AND MANY PAPERS IN PARK
POLLUTION SO BAD

MICHELLE TOMEK
7yrs

A NOTE ON HAIKU POETRY

For more than 500 years Japanese poets have been composing Haiku. Many of the greatest masterpieces of Japanese poetry are enshrined within this most diminutive of poetic forms. The Haiku is 3-line poetry composed of 17 syllables in length, 5-7-5. Each true Haiku is "a swift record in words of one moment"—a flash of lightning—a spontaneous conception. In its simplicity Haiku suggests much by saying little and is full of that wisdom that is to be found in the hearts of little children. Haiku, a national pastime in Japan, clearly reflects the Japanese love of nature and awareness that human beings are but one small part of all creation. To our students the East is neither vague nor indecipherable, but a living, relevant part of their world. For through the ennobling intimacy with Haiku we became inheritors of the spirit of its creators and became imbued with its approach to life. Haiku revealed the sacredness of all life and disclosed our kinship with all living things. Moreover, it unveiled those intangible realities of beauty which lead to the immutable values that give us the capacity to endure.

This book of poetry, written and illustrated by Wilhelm students, 4 to 8 years of age, is tangible evidence of the enlargement of their world.

Marilyn E. Wilhelm

THE WILHELM SCHOLÊ
3611 Cummins Lane
Houston, Texas 77027

The Wilhelm Scholê is an American school for
children of all nations. The students are 2 to 12
years of age and include children of 20
different nations and 9 different religions.

"how to think, not what to think"